Who Made This Mess?

Alison Hawes

Illustrated by Kay Widdowson

OXFORD
UNIVERSITY PRESS

"What a mess!" said Mum.
"Is this your mess, Little Dragon?"

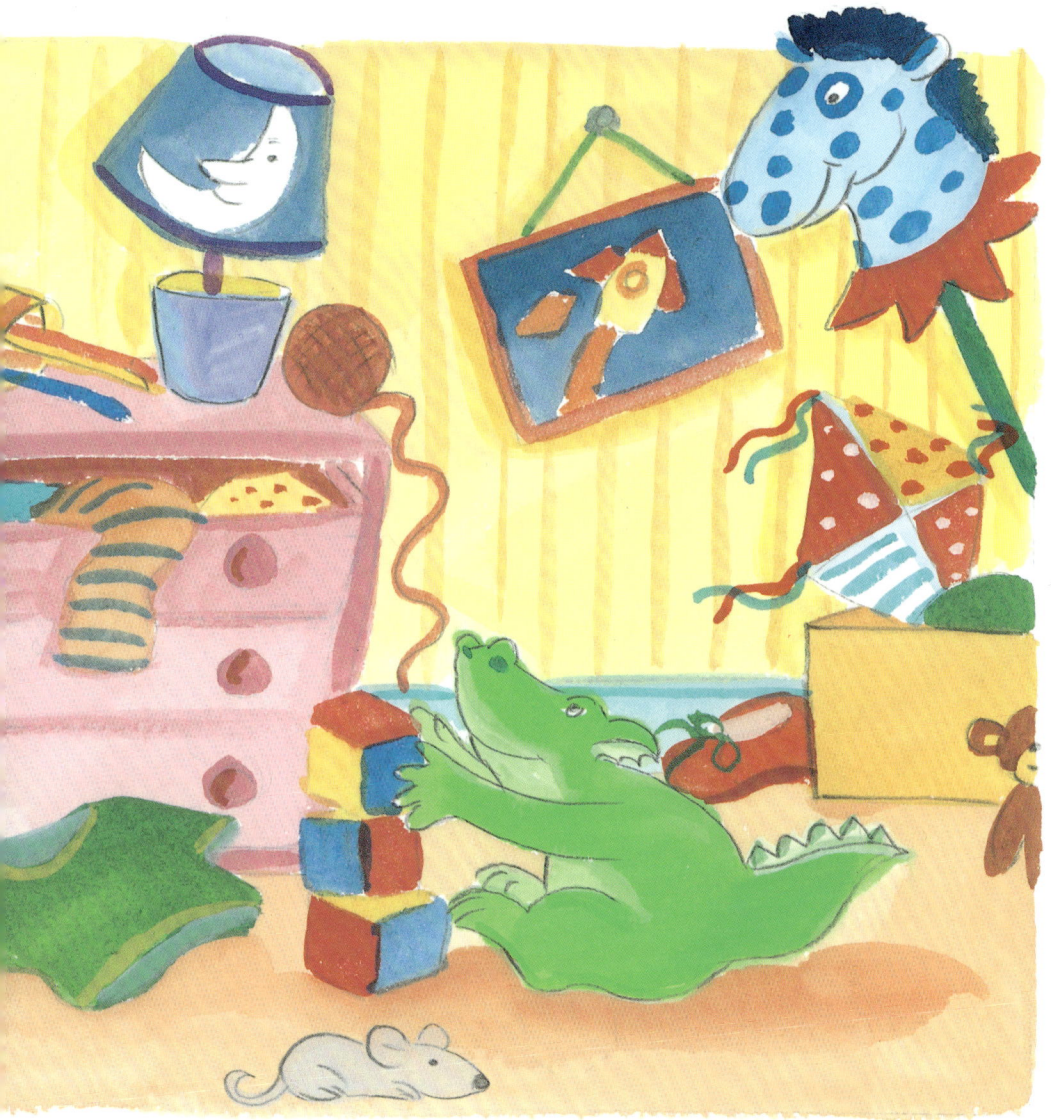

"It's not my mess,"
said Little Dragon.
"It's his mess!"

"Now, Little Dragon," said Mum.
"A lot of this mess is yours."

"No, it's not my mess,"
said Little Dragon.
"It's his mess!"

"Now, Little Dragon," said Mum.
"Is this your green tee-shirt?"

"No, it's not my tee-shirt,"
said Little Dragon.
"It's his tee-shirt!"

"No, Little Dragon," said Mum.
"It **is** your tee-shirt."

"Now, Little Dragon," said Mum.
"Is this your red shoe?"

"No, it's not my shoe,"
  said Little Dragon.
"It's his shoe!"

"No, Little Dragon," said Mum.
"It **is** your shoe."

"Now, Little Dragon," said Mum.
"Is this your yellow hat?"

"No, it's not my hat,"
said Little Dragon.
"It's his hat!"

"Now, Little Dragon," said Mum.
"Are these your sweets?"

Sweets!

"Yes!" said Little Dragon.
"They are **my** sweets!"

"Help me tidy up the mess,"
said Mum.
"Then we can share the sweets."

Late for School

Alison Hawes

Illustrated by Kay Widdowson

OXFORD

UNIVERSITY PRESS

Little Dragon looked at the clock.

It was nine o'clock.
"Oh no!" said Little Dragon.

She pulled on her school trousers.

She pulled on her school tee-shirt.

She pulled on her green
school jumper.

She pulled on some blue socks.

She ran downstairs.

She ran into the kitchen.

She had some cornflakes.
She had some toast and jam.

She ran upstairs.
She ran to the bathroom.

She brushed her teeth.
She brushed her hair.

She put on some shoes.
She put on her blue school coat.

She ran to school.

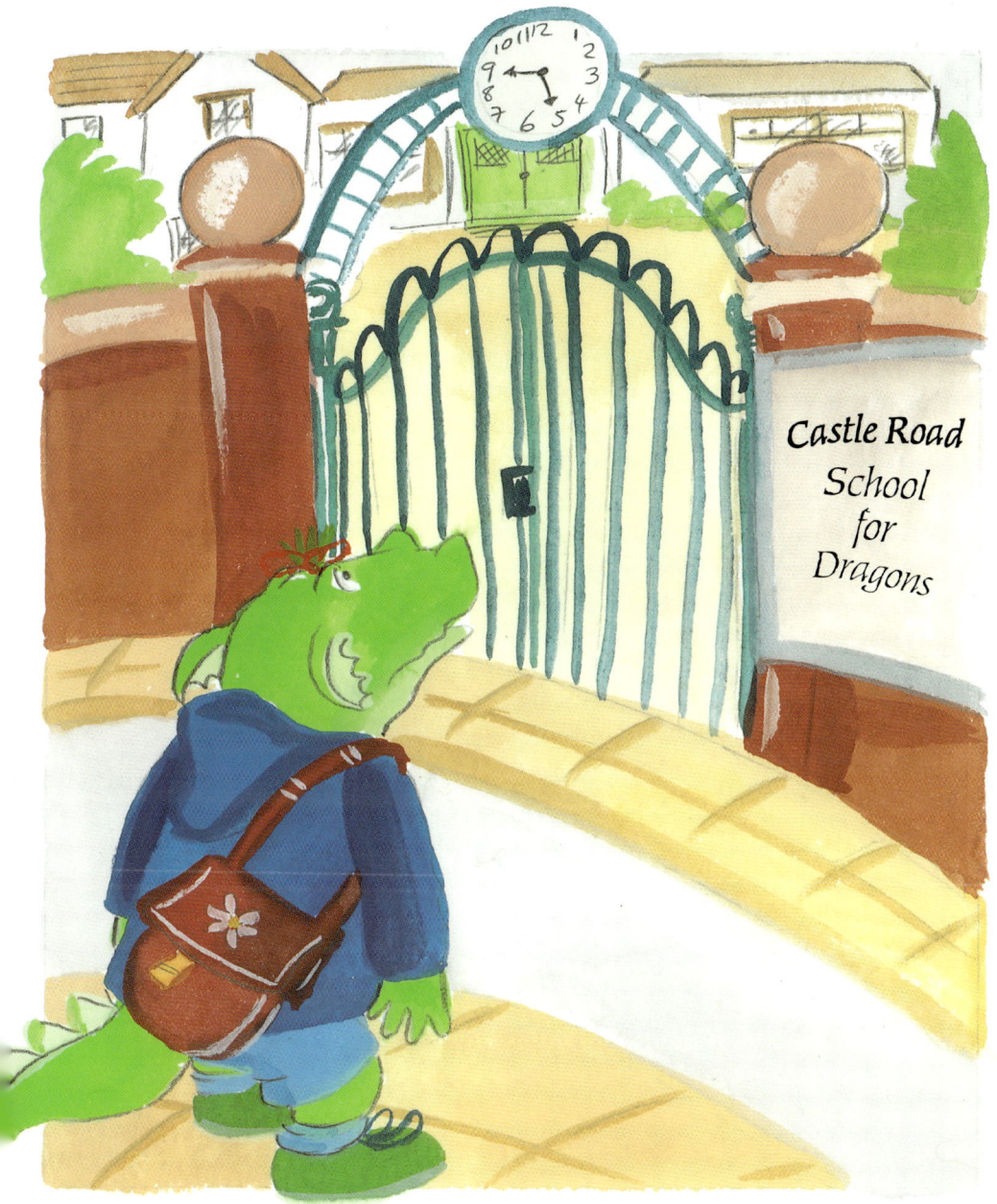

Castle Road
School
for
Dragons

The school was closed.

"Oh no!" said Little Dragon.
It was Sunday.